OCR GCSE MATHEMATICS

STAGE 7

GRADUATED ASSESSMENT

SECOND EDITION

- Howard Baxter
- Michael Handbury
- John Jeskins
- Jean Matthews
- Mark Patmore

Hodder Murray

www.hoddereducation.co.uk

Hodder Headline's policy is to use papers that are natural, renewable and recyclable products and made from wood grown in sustainable forests. The logging and manufacturing processes are expected to conform to the environmental regulations of the country of origin.

Orders: please contact Bookpoint Ltd, 130 Milton Park, Abingdon, Oxon OX14 4SB. Telephone: (44) 01235 827720. Fax: (44) 01235 400454. Lines are open 9 a.m. to 5 p.m., Monday to Saturday, with a 24-hour message-answering service. Visit our website at www.hoddereducation.co.uk.

Personal Tutor CD-ROM © Howard Baxter, Michael Handbury, John Jeskins, Jean Matthews, Mark Patmore, Brian Seager, Eddie Wilde, 2007; with contributions from Andy Sturman; developed by Infuze Limited; cast: Nicolette Landau; recorded at Alchemy Soho

First published in 2007 by
Hodder Murray, an imprint of Hodder Education,
a member of the Hodder Headline Group, an Hachette Livre UK company,
338 Euston Road
London NW1 3BH

Impression number   10 9 8 7 6 5 4 3 2
Year   2012 2011 2010 2009 2008 2007

Cover photo © Andy Sacks/Photographer's Choice/Getty Images
Typeset in 10pt Times Ten Roman by Tech-Set Ltd. Gateshead, Tyne and Wear.
Printed in Great Britain by CPI Antony Rowe

A catalogue record for this title is available from the British Library

ISBN: 978 0340 91589 9

Contents

STAGE

7

Introduction

This book contains exercises designed to be used with the Graduated Assessment for OCR GCSE Mathematics course. The work covers Stage 7 of the specification.

Each exercise matches an exercise in the Graduated Assessment for OCR GCSE Mathematics Stage 7 Student's Book. The exercises in the textbook are numbered through each chapter. For instance, in Chapter 16, Exercise 16.2 is on tangents to a circle. The corresponding homework exercise is Exercise 16.2H.

You will find that the homework exercises are generally shorter than those in the Student's Book but still cover the same mathematics. Some questions are intended to be completed without a calculator, just as in the Student's Book. These are shown with a non-calculator icon in the same way. Doing these questions without a calculator is vital practice for the non-calculator sections of the module test and the GCSE examination papers.

The Homework Book gives you the opportunity for further practice on the work undertaken in class. It is also a smaller book to carry home! If you have understood the topics, you should be able to tackle these exercises confidently as they are no harder than the ones you have done in class.

More practice helps to reinforce the ideas you have learned and makes them easier to remember at a later stage. If, however, you do forget, further help is at hand. As well as the textbook, there is also, with this book, a Personal Tutor CD-ROM. This contains worked examples on key topics to revise concepts you find difficult and consolidate your understanding. The exercises supported with examples on the Personal Tutor CD-ROM are marked with an icon.

You will find the answers to this Homework Book in the Foundation and Higher Assessment Packs.

Coordinates

STAG
7

EXERCISE 1.1H

pt

1 For each of the lines in the diagram, find the coordinates of the midpoint.

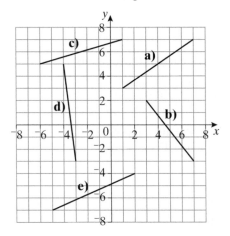

2 Find the coordinates of the midpoint of the line joining each of these pairs of points.

a) A(3, 7) and B(⁻5, 7) **b)** C(2, 1) and D(8, 5)
c) E(3, 7) and F(8, 2) **d)** G(1, 6) and H(9, 3)
e) I(⁻7, 1) and J(3, 6) **f)** K(⁻5, ⁻6) and L(⁻7, ⁻3)

EXERCISE 1.2H

1 OABCDEFG is a cuboid.
F is the point (5, 7, 3).

Write down the coordinates of each of these points.

a) A   **b)** B   **c)** C
d) D   **e)** E   **f)** G

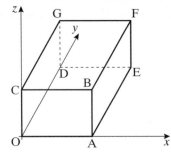

2 OABCV is a pyramid with a rectangular base.
V is directly above the centre of the base, N.
OA = 8 units, AB = 10 units and VN = 7 units.

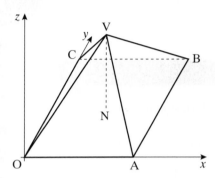

Write down the coordinates of each of these points.

a) A   **b)** B   **c)** C   **d)** N   **e)** V

3 OABCDEFG is a cuboid.
M is the midpoint of BF and N is the midpoint of GF.
OA = 6 units, OC = 5 units and OD = 3 units.

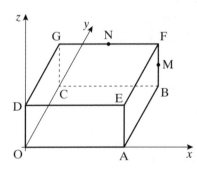

a) Write down the coordinates of each of these points.

    (i) B   **(ii)** F   **(iii)** G   **(iv)** M   **(v)** N

b) (i) The point $(6, 2\frac{1}{2}, 0)$ is the midpoint of which edge?

    (ii) The point $(0, 2\frac{1}{2}, 1\frac{1}{2})$ is the centre of which face?

Percentages

EXERCISE 2.1H

1 Change each of these percentages to a fraction.
Write your answers in their lowest terms.

   a) 45%   **b)** 75%   **c)** 12%   **d)** 110%

2 Change each of these percentages to a decimal.

   a) 19%   **b)** 40%   **c)** 9%   **d)** 17·5%

3 Change each of these decimals to a percentage.

   a) 0·47   **b)** 0·82   **c)** 0·04   **d)** 0·425   **e)** 1·35

4 Copy and complete this table.

Fraction	Decimal	Percentage
$\frac{3}{10}$		
$\frac{3}{5}$		
$\frac{7}{20}$		
$\frac{3}{8}$		
$\frac{5}{6}$		

5 Change each of these fractions to a decimal.

   a) $\frac{19}{100}$ **b)** $\frac{9}{50}$ **c)** $\frac{13}{20}$ **d)** $\frac{3}{100}$ **e)** $\frac{7}{4}$

6 Change each of these fractions to a percentage.
Where necessary, give your answer correct to
1 decimal place.

   a) $\frac{6}{100}$ **b)** $\frac{3}{50}$ **c)** $\frac{7}{8}$ **d)** $\frac{9}{5}$ **e)** $\frac{3}{11}$

EXERCISE 2.2H

1 Jane earns £5 per hour.
   She receives a pay increase of 25p per hour.
   Calculate her pay increase as a percentage of £5.

2 A television originally costing £150 is reduced by £30.
   Calculate the reduction as a percentage of the original price.

3 Craig bought a printer costing £56 before VAT.
   What was the price after VAT at 17·5% was added on?

4 In a sale, all the prices are reduced by 35%.
   A coat was priced at £65 before the sale.
   What was the sale price of the coat?

5 A car was bought for £9000.
   A year later it was sold for £7500.
   Calculate the loss in value as a percentage of £9000.
   Give your answer to the nearest whole number.

Ratio and proportion

STAG
7

EXERCISE 3.1H

1 Write each of these ratios in its lowest terms.

a) $3 : 33$ **b)** $20 : 48$ **c)** $32 : 84$
d) $16 : 32 : 64$ **e)** $15 : 45 : 85$

2 Write each of these ratios in its lowest terms.

a) 12 m $: 8$ cm   **b)** 420 ml $: 2$ litres
c) 600 g $: 6$ kg   **d)** 50p $: £8·50$
e) $1\frac{1}{2}$ hours $: 50$ minutes

3 At a school there are 425 girls and 375 boys.
Write the ratio of girls to boys in its lowest terms.

4 300 ml of concentrated orange are mixed with
1·5 litres of water.
Write the ratio of concentrated orange to water in its
lowest terms.

5 A recipe for bread uses 5 g of dried yeast, 40 g of
butter and 1 kg of flour.
Write the ratio of the ingredients in its lowest terms.

EXERCISE 3.2H

1 To make a dressing for her lawn, Rachel mixes loam
and sand in the ratio $1 : 3$.

a) How much sand should she mix with two buckets
of loam?

b) How much loam should she mix with 15 buckets
of sand?

2 To make mortar, Fred mixes 1 part cement with 5 parts sand.

  a) How much sand does he mix with 500 g of cement?

  b) How much cement does he mix with 4·5 kg of sand?

3 A rectangular picture is 6 cm wide.
It is enlarged in the ratio 1 : 4.
How wide is the enlargement?

4 To decorate his bathroom, Callum uses blue and white tiles in the ratio 1 : 6.

  a) On the side of the bath he uses twelve blue tiles.
  How many white tiles does he use?

  b) In the shower he uses 240 white tiles.
  How many blue tiles does he use?

5 Harry mixes 3 parts black paint with 4 parts white paint to make dark grey paint.

  a) How much white paint does he mix with 150 ml of black paint?

  b) How much black paint does he mix with 1 litre of white paint?

6 A plan of a wood is drawn using a scale of 2 centimetres to 50 metres.

  a) On the plan, the wood is 24 cm wide.
  What is the real width of the wood?

  b) The real length of the wood is 950 m.
  What is the length of the wood on the plan?

7 Two photographs are in the ratio 3 to 4.

  a) The smaller photograph is 9 cm high.
  How high is the larger photograph?

  b) The larger photograph is 8·4 cm wide.
  How wide is the smaller photograph?

8 In an election the number of votes was shared between the Labour, Conservative and other parties in the ratio 5 : 4 : 2.
Labour received 7500 votes.

  a) How many votes did the Conservatives receive?

  b) How many votes did the other parties receive?

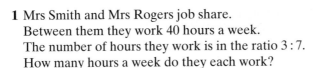

EXERCISE 3.3H

Do not use your calculator for questions **1** to **5**.

1 Mrs Smith and Mrs Rogers job share.
Between them they work 40 hours a week.
The number of hours they work is in the ratio $3:7$.
How many hours a week do they each work?

2 Paint is mixed in the ratio 2 parts black paint to 3 parts white paint
to make 10 litres of grey paint.

a) How much black paint is used?

b) How much white paint is used?

3 A casserole uses meat, onion and carrot in the ratio $4:1:3$.
How much of each ingredient is there in 1 kg of casserole?

4 Sarah is a nurse. She worked 7 hours one day.
The time she spent on administration, working on the wards and
working in theatre is in the ratio $2:5:7$.
How long did she spend working on the wards?

5 Daisy and Emily invested £5000 and £8000 respectively in a
business venture.
They agreed to share the profits in the ratio of their investment.
Emily received £320.
What was the total profit?

You may use your calculator for questions **6** to **8**.

6 Keith, Martine and Ruby share a lottery win in the ratio $5:3:7$.
The prize is £1800.
How much does Ruby receive?

7 A large jar of sweets contains red, yellow and orange sweets in the
ratio $9:7:8$.
There are 576 sweets in the jar.
How many orange sweets are there?

8 Iain and Stephen bought a house between them in Spain.
Iain paid 60% of the cost and Stephen paid 40%.

a) Write the ratio of the amounts they paid in its lowest terms.

b) The house cost 210 000 euros. How much did each pay?

STAG

7

EXERCISE 3.4H

1 An 80 g bag of Munchies costs 99p and a 200 g bag of Munchies costs £2·19.
Show which is the better value.

2 Baxter's lemonade is sold in 2-litre bottles for £1·29 and in 3-litre bottles for £1·99.
Show which is the better value.

3 Butter is sold in 200 g tubs for 95p and in 450 g packets for £2·10.
Show which is the better value.

4 Fruit yogurt is sold in packs of 4 tubs for 79p and in packs of 12 tubs for £2·19.
Show which is the better value.

5 There are two packs of minced meat on the reduced price shelf at the supermarket: a 1·8 kg pack reduced to £2·50 and a 1·5 kg pack reduced to £2.
Show which is the better value.

6 Smoothie shaving gel costs £1·19 for the 75 ml bottle and £2·89 for the 200 ml bottle.
Show which is the better value.

7 A supermarket sells cans of cola in two different sized packs: a pack of 12 cans costs £4·30 and a pack of 20 cans costs £7·25.
Show which is the better value.

8 Sudso washing powder is sold in three sizes: 750 g for £3·15, 1·5 kg for £5·99 and 2·5 kg for £6·99.
Show which is the better value.

Probability

4

EXERCISE 4.1H

1 James has ten T-shirts. Three of them have logos.
He takes a T-shirt without looking.
What is the probability that the T-shirt has a logo?

2 There are five green balls, seven red balls and four
black balls in a bag.
Hollie takes one out without looking.
What is the probability that it is

a) green?   **b)** red?   **c)** not red?

3 The probability that in a family with three children
they are all boys is $\frac{1}{8}$.
What is the probability that they are not all boys?

4 The probability that Emily remembers to bring her
homework to school is 0·98.
What is the probability that she forgets her
homework?

5 Alison has a bag of sweets which contains 5 sherbet
lemons, 9 chocolate éclairs and 11 wine gums.
She takes one out without looking.
Find the probability that it is

a) a sherbet lemon.

b) not a chocolate éclair.

6 A football coach is choosing a striker for the next
game.
He has three players to choose from: Wayne,
Michael and Alan.
The probability that he will choose Wayne is $\frac{5}{19}$
and the probability that he will choose Michael is $\frac{7}{19}$.
What is the probability that he will choose Alan?

7 The probability of a baby being a boy is $\frac{1}{2}$.
Mr and Mrs Brown decide to have two children.
List all the possible outcomes and find the probability of having two girls.

8 A normal dice is rolled and a coin is tossed.

a) List all the possible outcomes.

b) Calculate the probability of getting
   (i) a six and a head.
   (ii) a tail and a prime number.

9 Elaine goes to town by car, bus, taxi or bike.
The probability that she uses her car is $\frac{12}{31}$, the probability that she catches the bus is $\frac{2}{31}$ and the probability that she takes a taxi is $\frac{13}{31}$.
What is the probability that she rides her bike into town?

10 A cash bag contains only £20, £10 and £5 notes.
One note is chosen from the bag at random.
There is a probability of $\frac{3}{4}$ that it is a £5 note and a probability of $\frac{3}{20}$ that it is a £10 note.
What is the probability that it is a £20 note?

▌▐▐▐ EXERCISE 4.2H

1 The probability that United will lose their next game is 0·2.
How many games would you expect them to lose in a season of 40 games?

2 The probability that it will rain on any day in June is $\frac{2}{15}$.
On how many of June's 30 days would you expect it to rain?

3 The probability that an eighteen-year-old driver will have an accident is 0·15.
There are 80 eighteen-year-old drivers in a school.
How many of them might be expected to have an accident?

4 When Phil is playing chess, the probability that he wins is $\frac{17}{20}$.
In a competition, Phil plays ten games.
How many of them might you expect him to win?

5 An ordinary six-sided dice is thrown 90 times.
How many times might you expect to get

a) a 4?   **b)** an odd number?

6 A box contains twelve yellow balls, three blue balls and five green balls.
A ball is chosen at random and its colour noted.
The ball is then replaced. This is done 400 times.
How many of each colour might you expect to get?

EXERCISE 4.3H

1 Pete rolls a dice 200 times and records the number of times each score appears.

Score	1	2	3	4	5	6
Frequency	29	34	35	32	34	36

a) Work out the relative frequency of each of the scores.
Give your answers to 2 decimal places.

b) Do you think that Pete's dice is fair?
Give a reason for your answer.

2 Rory kept a record of his favourite football team's results.
They won 32 of their matches, drew 11 and lost 7.

a) Calculate the relative frequency of each of the three outcomes.

b) Are your answers to part **a)** good estimates for the probability of each of the outcomes?
Give a reason for your answer.

3 In a survey, 600 people were asked which flavour of crisps they preferred. The results are shown in the table.

Flavour	Frequency
Plain	166
Salt and vinegar	130
Cheese and onion	228
Other	76

a) Work out the relative frequency for each flavour.
Give your answers to 2 decimal places.

b) Explain why it is reasonable to use these figures to estimate the probability of the flavour of crisps that the next person to be asked will prefer.

STAG

7

4 The owner of a petrol station notices that in one day 287 out of
340 people filling their car with petrol spent over £20.
Use these figures to estimate the probability that the next
customer will spend

a) over £20.

b) £20 or less.

5 Jasmine made a spinner numbered 1, 2, 3, 4 and 5.
She tested the spinner to see if it was fair.
The results are shown below.

Score	1	2	3	4	5
Frequency	46	108	203	197	96

a) Work out the relative frequency of each of the scores.
Give your answers to 2 decimal places.

b) Do you think that the spinner is fair?
Give a reason for your answer.

6 A box contains yellow, green, white and blue counters.
A counter is chosen from the box and its colour noted.
The counter is then replaced in the box.
The table below gives information about the colour of counter
picked.

Colour	Yellow	Green	White	Blue
Relative frequency	0·4	0·3	0·225	0·075

a) There are 80 counters altogether in the bag.
How many do you think there are of each colour?

b) What other information is needed before you can be sure that
your answers to part **a)** are accurate?

TAGE

7

Using and generating formulae

5

Write a formula for each of these using the letters given.

1 The cost (£C) of buying m kg of meat at £q per kg.

2 The average speed (s) of a journey is the total distance (d) divided by the time (t).

3 A two-digit number (n) is 10 times the tens digit (t) plus the units digit (u).

4 The mean (m) of three numbers p, q and r is the total of the three numbers divided by 3.

5 Take home pay (p) is the number of hours worked (h) multiplied by the rate per hour (r), minus the tax (t).

6 The total amount saved (£t) when Tim saves £4·50 for w weeks.

7 The number (n) of 3-metre strips of paper that can be cut from a roll of paper r metres long.

8 The sale price (£s) of a computer when a discount (£d) is taken off the normal price (£n).

9 A taxi company works out the fare (£f) by dividing the distance covered (d kilometres) by 5 and then adding 3.

10 The total cost (£C) of a school outing for s students when the coach costs £400 to hire and the entrance fee is £7 for each student.

STAG

7

pt You may find the example useful for Exercises 5.2H and 5.3H.

EXERCISE 5.2H

Use the formulae in Exercise 5.1H to find each of these.

1 C when $m = 2 \cdot 5$ kg and $q = £6$

2 s when $d = 200$ miles and $t = 5$ hours

3 n when $t = 5$ and $u = 3$

4 m when $p = 16$, $q = 20$ and $r = 9$

5 p when $h = 40$ hours, $r = £6$ per hour and $t = £35$

6 t when $w = 12$ weeks

7 n when $r = 24$ m

8 s when $d = £150$ and $n = £599$

9 f when $d = 4 \cdot 5$ km

10 C when $s = 23$

EXERCISE 5.3H

Work out the value of each of these formulae for the values given.

Do not use your calculator for questions **1** to **6**.

1 $v = u + at$ when $u = 6$, $a = 4$ and $t = \frac{1}{2}$

2 $z = 4y - 5x$ when $y = 7$ and $x = {}^-2$

3 $k = fh + \dfrac{g}{h}$ when $f = 1 \cdot 2$, $g = 3 \cdot 5$ and $h = 0 \cdot 5$

4 $b = a^2 - c^3$ when $a = {}^-5$ and $c = {}^-3$

5 $p = \dfrac{a}{2bc}$ when $a = 6$, $b = \frac{3}{4}$ and $c = {}^-2$

6 $y = mx^2 + c$ when $m = 3$, $x = {}^-12$ and $c = 6$

You may use your calculator for questions **7** to **10**.

Give your answers correct to 2 decimal places.

7 $h = 3c^3 + f$ when $c = 8$ and $f = 7$

8 $y = 3x^3 + 2x^2 + c$ when $x = 2 \cdot 2$ and $c = 4 \cdot 7$

9 $z = 5x^2 - 2y^2$ when $x = {}^-6 \cdot 7$ and $y = {}^-3 \cdot 2$

10 $a = \dfrac{b^2 + 6cd}{c + d}$ when $b = 0 \cdot 4$, $c = 0 \cdot 25$ and $d = 5$

Solving angle problems

6

You may find the example useful for Exercises 6.1H and 6.2H.

EXERCISE 6.1H

Find the size of each lettered angle in these diagrams, giving your reasons.

1

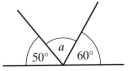

5

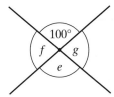

2

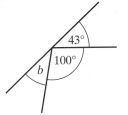

6

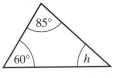

3

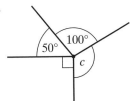

7

4

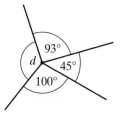

8

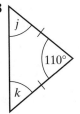

9

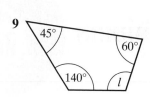

45°

60°

140° *l*

10

72°

n

80° *m*

104°

EXERCISE 6.2H

Find the size of each lettered angle, giving your reasons.

1

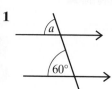

a

60°

6

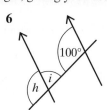

100°

h *i*

2

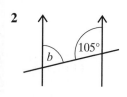

b

105°

7

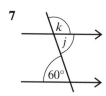

k

j

60°

3

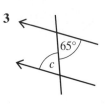

65°

c

8

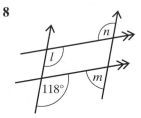

n

l

m

118°

4

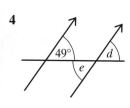

49° *d*

e

9

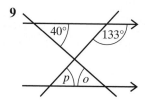

40° 133°

p *o*

5

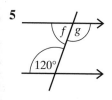

f *g*

120°

10

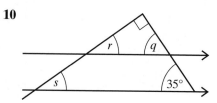

r *q*

s 35°

EXERCISE 6.3H

1 A polygon has nine sides.
Work out the sum of the interior angles of this polygon.

2 A polygon has 13 sides.
Work out the sum of the interior angles of this polygon.

3 Four of the exterior angles of a hexagon are 93°, 50°, 37° and 85°.
The other two angles are equal.

a) Work out the size of these equal exterior angles.

b) Work out the interior angles of the hexagon.

4 Four of the interior angles of a pentagon are 170°, 80°, 157° and 75°.

a) Work out the size of the other interior angle.

b) Work out the exterior angles of the pentagon.

5 A regular polygon has 18 sides.
Find the size of the exterior and the interior angle of this polygon.

6 A regular polygon has 24 sides.
Find the size of the exterior and the interior angle of this polygon.

7 A regular polygon has an exterior angle of 12°.
Work out the number of sides that the polygon has.

8 A regular polygon has an interior angle of 172°.
Work out the number of sides that the polygon has.

EXERCISE 6.4H

Find the size of each lettered angle.

1

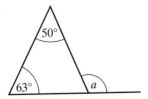

2

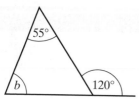

3

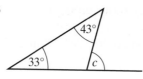

4

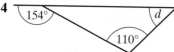

5

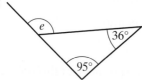

6

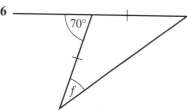

7

8

Direct proportion

1 Calculate the missing values in each of these tables, where y is proportional to x.

a)

x	8	4	
y	20		30

b)

x	4		19
y	5	8·75	

2 Use the table to find out if y is proportional to x.

x	20	25	45	50
y	36	45	81	90

3 y is proportional to x.
Use the table to find the equation connecting x and y.

x	40	30
y	16	12

4 Calculate the missing value in each of these tables, where y is proportional to x.
Find also the equation connecting x and y for each table.

a)

x	4	7	10
y	28	49	

b)

x	20	90	142
y	26	117	

5 *y* is proportional to *x*.
When $x = 6$, $y = 9$.

a) Find the value of *y* when $x = 13$.

b) Find the value of *x* when $y = 36$.

6 *h* is proportional to *f*.
When $f = 8$, $h = 4·8$.

a) Find the value of *h* when $f = 5$.

b) Find the value of *f* when $h = 13·2$.

7 A ladder that is 7 metres long has 28 rungs.
How many rungs would a ladder that is 5 metres long have?

8 A landscape gardener can paint 15 fence panels in 6 hours.
How long would it take him to paint 40 fence panels?

9 The cost of 12 printer cartridges is £90·00.
What is the cost of 5 of these cartridges?

10 A van uses £18 worth of petrol for a journey of 75 miles.

a) What is the cost of petrol for a journey of 120 miles?

b) The van is empty of petrol.
The driver has just £10.
Can he buy enough petrol to cover the 45 miles back home?

Checking solutions and calculations

EXERCISE 8.1H

Do not use your calculator for questions **1** to **3**.

1 These calculations are all wrong.
This can be spotted quickly without working them out.
For each one, give a reason why it is wrong.

a) $15 \cdot 3 \div {}^-5 \cdot 1 = 5$ **b)** $8 \cdot 7 \times 1 \cdot 6 = 5 \cdot 4375$

c) $4 \cdot 7 \times 300 = 9400$ **d)** $7 \cdot 5^2 = 46 \cdot 25$

e) $5 \cdot 400 \div 9 = 60$ **f)** ${}^-6 \cdot 2 \times {}^-0 \cdot 5 = {}^-93 \cdot 1$

g) $\sqrt{0 \cdot 4} = 0 \cdot 2$ **h)** $8 \cdot 5 \times 7 \cdot 1 = 60 \cdot 36$

2 Estimate the answers to each of these calculations.
Show your working.

a) 93×108 **b)** $0 \cdot 61^2$ **c)** ${}^-19 \cdot 6 + 5 \cdot 2$

3 Estimate the answers to each of these calculations.
Show your working.

a) The cost of three DVDs at £17·99.

b) The cost of 39 cinema tickets at £6·20.

c) The cost of five meals at £7·99 and two drinks at
£2·10.

You may use your calculator for question **4**.

4 Use inverse operations to check these calculations.
Write down the operations you use.

a) $19\,669 \cdot 5 \div 235 = 83 \cdot 7$

b) $\sqrt{5069 \cdot 44} = 71 \cdot 2$

c) $9 \cdot 7 \times 12 \cdot 4 = 120 \cdot 28$

d) $17 \cdot 2 \times 4 \cdot 6 + 68 \cdot 2 = 147 \cdot 32$

EXERCISE 8.2H

Round each of these numbers to 1 significant figure.

1 14·3	**6** 0·78	**11** 8·4	**16** 0·71
2 38	**7** 0·61	**12** 18·36	**17** 0·0052
3 6·54	**8** 0·053	**13** 725	**18** 0·019
4 308	**9** 2413·5	**14** 8032	**19** 407·511
5 1210	**10** 0·0097	**15** 98·3	**20** 23 095

EXERCISE 8.3H

Find an approximate answer to each of the calculations in questions **1** to **27** by rounding each number to 1 significant figure.
Show your working.

1 223·7 + 387·2

2 719 ÷ 81·6

3 18·2 × 53·7

4 692²

5 $\dfrac{94·6}{3·7 \times 21·7}$

6 61·7 × 5·8

7 3·7 × 9·1

8 23·127 × 28·4

9 73·4 × 46·8

10 $\dfrac{17·8 \times 5·7}{39·2}$

11 $\sqrt{9·7 \times 11·2}$

12 0·82 × 27·3

13 $\dfrac{0·58 \times 73·4}{6·12}$

14 21·2³

15 189 × 0·31

16 $\sqrt{11·1^2 - 4·8^2}$

17 $\dfrac{51 \cdot 8 + 39 \cdot 2}{0 \cdot 022}$

18 71×58

19 $\sqrt{46}$

20 $\dfrac{5987}{5 \cdot 1}$

21 $19 \cdot 1^2$

22 $62 \cdot 7 \times 8316$

23 $\dfrac{5 \cdot 72}{19 \cdot 3}$

24 $\dfrac{32}{49 \cdot 4}$

25 8152×37

26 $\dfrac{935 \times 41}{8 \cdot 5}$

27 $\dfrac{673 \times 0 \cdot 76}{3 \cdot 6 \times 2 \cdot 38}$

28 A new computer is priced at £595 excluding VAT.
VAT at 17·5% must be paid on it.
Estimate the amount of VAT to be paid.

29 A square paving slab has an area of 6000 cm².
Estimate the length of a side of the slab.

30 A circle has radius 4·3 cm.
Estimate its area.

9 Scatter diagrams and correlation

1 Bill grows tomatoes. As an experiment he divided his
land into eight plots.
He used a different amount of fertiliser on each plot.
The table shows the weight of tomatoes he got from
each of the plots.

Amount of fertiliser (g/m²)	Weight of tomatoes (kg)
10	36
20	41
30	58
40	60
50	70
60	76
70	75
80	92

a) Draw a scatter diagram to show this information.

b) Describe the correlation shown in the scatter
diagram.

c) Draw a line of best fit on your scatter diagram.

d) What weight of tomatoes should Bill expect to get
if he uses 75 g/m² of fertiliser?

2 The table at the top of the next page shows the prices
and mileages of seven second-hand cars of the same
model.

a) Draw a scatter diagram to show this information.

b) Describe the correlation shown in the scatter
diagram.

Price (£)	Mileage
6000	27 000
3500	69 000
1000	92 000
8500	17 000
5500	53 000
3500	82 000
6000	43 000

c) Draw a line of best fit on your scatter diagram.

d) Use your line of best fit to estimate
    (i) the price of this model of car which has covered 18 000 miles.
    (ii) the mileage of this model of car which costs £4000.

3 The heights of ten daughters, all aged 20, and their fathers are given in the table.

Height of father (cm)	Height of daughter (cm)
167	164
168	166
169	166
171	168
172	169
172	170
174	170
175	171
176	173
182	177

a) Draw a scatter diagram to show this information.

b) Describe the correlation shown in the scatter diagram.

c) Draw a line of best fit on your scatter diagram.

d) Use your line of best fit to estimate the height of a 20-year-old daughter whose father is 180 cm tall.

Pythagoras' theorem

EXERCISE 10.1H

Calculate the missing area in each of these diagrams.

1

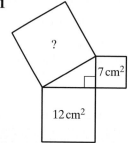

3

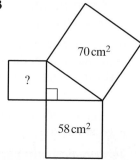

2

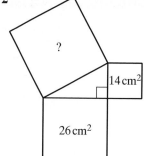

4

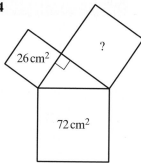

You may find the example useful for Exercises 10.2H and 10.3H.

▌▌▌ EXERCISE 10.2H

Find the length of the hypotenuse, x, in each of these triangles.
Give your answers either exactly or correct to 2 decimal places.

1

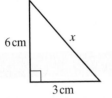

6 cm

x

3 cm

3

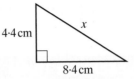

4·4 cm

x

8·4 cm

2

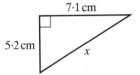

7·1 cm

5·2 cm

x

4

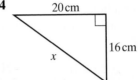

20 cm

16 cm

x

▌▌▌ EXERCISE 10.3H

Find the length marked x in each of these triangles.
Give your answers either exactly or correct to 2 decimal places.

1

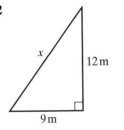

x

7 cm

13 cm

2

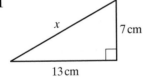

x

12 m

9 m

3

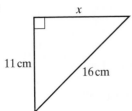

x

11 cm

16 cm

4

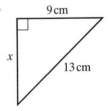

9 cm

x

13 cm

5

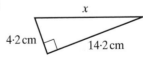

x

4·2 cm

14·2 cm

6

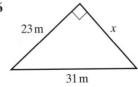

23 m

x

31 m

7

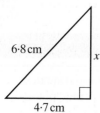

6·8 cm

x

4·7 cm

8

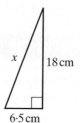

x

18 cm

6·5 cm

EXERCISE 10.4H

1 Ann can walk home from school along two roads or along a path across a field.

How much shorter is her journey if she takes the path across the field?

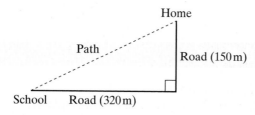

Home

Path

Road (150 m)

School Road (320 m)

2 This network is made of wire.

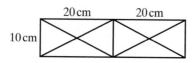

20 cm   20 cm

10 cm

What is the total length of wire?

3 A ladder 10 m long has its base 3 m from the foot of a vertical wall.

How far up the wall will the ladder reach?

4 The sides of a rectangle are 5 cm and 6 cm long.

Find the length of the diagonal of the rectangle.

5 An aircraft flies 120 km South, then 150 km East, then 200 km North.

How far is the aircraft from its starting position?

EXERCISE 10.5H

State whether or not each of these triangles is right-angled.
Show your working.

1

15 cm 20 cm
25 cm

5

8 m
11 m
7 m

2

7·3 m 4·2 m
8·7 m

6

6·5 m
12·8 m
11·1 m

3

12 cm 12 cm
15 cm

7

8·4 cm
30 cm
28·8 cm

4

40·3 cm
15·5 cm 37·2 cm

8

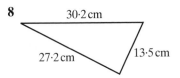

30·2 cm
27·2 cm 13·5 cm

Quadratic graphs

You may find the example useful for both of these exercises.

1 Copy and complete this table for $y = x^2 + 3x - 5$.
Do not draw the graph.

x				-2	-1	0	1	2	3	4	5
x^2											
$+3x$											
-5											
$y = x^2 + 3x - 5$											

2 a) Copy and complete this table for $y = x^2 + 2x$.

x		-3	-2	-1	0	1	2	3
x^2								
$+2x$								
$y = x^2 + 2x$								

b) Draw the graph of $y = x^2 + 2x$, for values of x from $^-3$ to 3.
Label the x-axis from $^-3$ to 3 and the y-axis from $^-2$ to 16.
Use a scale of 1 cm to 1 unit on the x-axis and 1 cm to 2 units on the y-axis.

3 Draw the graph of $y = x^2 - 5x + 6$, for values of x from $^-1$ to 6.

4 Draw the graph of $y = 2 + x - x^2$ for values of x from $^-3$ to 3.

5 Draw the graph of $y = 2x^2 - 3x - 1$ for values of x from $^-2$ to 3.

EXERCISE 11.2H

1 a) Draw the graph of $y = x^2 + 2x - 5$ for values of x from $^-5$ to 3.

b) Solve the equation $x^2 + 2x - 5 = 0$.

2 a) Draw the graph of $y = x^2 - 4x$ for values of x from $^-1$ to 5.

b) Solve the equation $x^2 - 4x = 0$.

c) Solve the equation $x^2 - 4x = ^-2$.

3 a) Draw the graph of $y = x^2 - 5x + 6$ for values of x from 0 to 5.

b) Solve the equation $x^2 - 5x + 6 = 0$.

c) Solve the equation $x^2 - 5x + 6 = 3$.

4 a) Draw the graph of $y = x^2 - 2x - 8$ for values of x from $^-3$ to 5.

b) Solve the equation $x^2 - 2x - 8 = 0$.

c) Solve the equation $x^2 - 2x - 8 = 5$.

d) Solve the equation $x^2 - 2x - 8 = ^-3$.

STAG

7

Finding the mean of grouped data

1 The table shows the number of trains arriving late at a station in the month of May.

Calculate an estimate of the mean number of trains late each day.

Number of trains arriving late each day	Frequency
0–4	18
5–9	9
10–14	3
15–19	0
20–24	1

2 The table shows the number of weeds per square metre in a survey site.

Calculate an estimate of the mean number of weeds per square metre.

Number of weeds per square metre	Frequency
0–14	204
15–29	101
30–44	39
45–59	13
60–74	6
75–89	2

3 The table shows the number of books sold each week by a book shop in one year.

Calculate an estimate of the mean number of books sold each week.

Number of books sold	Frequency
60–64	3
65–69	12
70–74	23
75–79	9
80–84	4
85–89	1

4 The table shows the number of days the students in Year 11 in a school were absent last year.

Calculate an estimate of the mean number of days' absence for the year.

Number of days' absence	Frequency
0–3	13
4–7	18
8–11	9
12–15	4
16–19	0
20–23	1
24–27	3

5 The table shows the number of sentences per chapter in a book.
Calculate an estimate of the mean number of sentences per chapter.

Number of sentences (x)	Frequency
$100 \leqslant x < 125$	1
$125 \leqslant x < 150$	9
$150 \leqslant x < 175$	8
$175 \leqslant x < 200$	5
$200 \leqslant x < 225$	2

6 A group of students were asked to estimate the number of beans in a jar.
The table shows the results of their estimates.
Calculate an estimate of the mean number of beans estimated by these students.

Estimated number of beans	Frequency
300–324	9
325–349	26
350–374	52
375–399	64
400–424	83
425–449	57
450–474	18
475–499	5

EXERCISE 12.2H

1 Calculate an estimate of the mean height of these sunflowers.

Height of sunflower in centimetres (x)	Frequency
$100 \leqslant x < 110$	6
$110 \leqslant x < 120$	13
$120 \leqslant x < 130$	35
$130 \leqslant x < 140$	29
$140 \leqslant x < 150$	16
$150 \leqslant x < 160$	11

2 Calculate an estimate of the mean weight of these eggs.

Weight of egg in grams (x)	Frequency
$20 \leqslant x < 25$	9
$25 \leqslant x < 30$	16
$30 \leqslant x < 35$	33
$35 \leqslant x < 40$	48
$40 \leqslant x < 45$	29
$45 \leqslant x < 50$	15

3 Calculate an estimate of the mean length of these green beans.

Length of green bean in millimetres (x)	Frequency
$60 \leqslant x < 80$	12
$80 \leqslant x < 100$	21
$100 \leqslant x < 120$	46
$120 \leqslant x < 140$	27
$140 \leqslant x < 160$	14

STAGE

7

4 Calculate an estimate of the mean time to finish the race.

Time to complete race in minutes (x)	Frequency
$54 \leqslant x < 56$	1
$56 \leqslant x < 58$	4
$58 \leqslant x < 60$	11
$60 \leqslant x < 62$	6
$62 \leqslant x < 64$	2
$64 \leqslant x < 66$	1

5 Calculate an estimate of the mean height of these shrubs.

Height of shrub in metres (x)	Frequency
$0 \cdot 3 \leqslant x < 0 \cdot 6$	57
$0 \cdot 6 \leqslant x < 0 \cdot 9$	41
$0 \cdot 9 \leqslant x < 1 \cdot 2$	36
$1 \cdot 2 \leqslant x < 1 \cdot 5$	24
$1 \cdot 5 \leqslant x < 1 \cdot 8$	15

6 Calculate an estimate of the mean weight of these plums.

Weight of plum in grams (x)	Frequency
$20 \leqslant x < 30$	6
$30 \leqslant x < 40$	19
$40 \leqslant x < 50$	58
$50 \leqslant x < 60$	15
$60 \leqslant x < 70$	4

7 Calculate an estimate of the mean length of these journeys.

Length of journey in minutes (x)	Frequency
$20 \leqslant x < 22$	6
$22 \leqslant x < 24$	20
$24 \leqslant x < 26$	38
$26 \leqslant x < 28$	47
$28 \leqslant x < 30$	16
$30 \leqslant x < 32$	3

8 Calculate an estimate of the mean speed of these cars.

Speed of car in miles per hour (x)	Frequency
$25 \leqslant x < 30$	4
$30 \leqslant x < 35$	29
$35 \leqslant x < 40$	33
$40 \leqslant x < 45$	6
$45 \leqslant x < 50$	2
$50 \leqslant x < 55$	1

9 Calculate an estimate of the mean wage of these workers.

Wages in £ (x)	Frequency
$500 \leqslant x < 1000$	3
$1000 \leqslant x < 1500$	14
$1500 \leqslant x < 2000$	18
$2000 \leqslant x < 2500$	5

10 Calculate an estimate of the mean length of these calls.

Length of call in seconds (x)	Frequency
$0 \leqslant x < 30$	51
$30 \leqslant x < 60$	25
$60 \leqslant x < 90$	13
$90 \leqslant x < 120$	7
$120 \leqslant x < 150$	4

STAG
7

13 Equations and inequalities 1

1 Write down the integer values of x when $^-5 \leqslant x < 3$.

Solve the inequalities in questions **2** to **15**.
For questions **2** to **5**, represent your solution on a number line.

2 $4x - 3 > 9$

3 $2(x - 1) < 6$

4 $1 - 3x \geqslant 10$

5 $0 \leqslant 2x - 3$

6 $5x < x + 8$

7 $2x \geqslant x - 5$

8 $4 + x < {}^-5$

9 $5x - 4 > 3x + 2$

10 $3x + 8 \leqslant 5x - 2$

11 $4x + 13 < 3(2x - 1)$

12 $2(x + 1) > x + 3$

13 $3x + 5 \leqslant 2x + 14$

14 $5x + 3 \leqslant 2x + 9$

15 $8x + 3 > 21 + 5x$

|||||| **EXERCISE 13.2H**

1 A teacher has £5 to spend on pens.
Pens cost 60p each.
She buys x pens.

   a) Write down an inequality in x.

   b) Solve your inequality to find the maximum number of pens she can buy.

2 One number is three times another.
Their sum is 24.

   a) Taking x as the smaller of the two numbers, write down an equation in x.

   b) Solve your equation to find the two numbers.

3 I think of a number, x, double it and add 11.
The answer is 37.

a) Write down an equation in x.

b) Solve your equation to find the number I first thought of.

4 When making sandwiches, it takes Bob 3 minutes to collect the ingredients he needs.
Once he has the ingredients, Bob can make a sandwich in 2 minutes.
Bob has 20 minutes to make as many sandwiches as he can.
Let the number of sandwiches he makes be x.
Write down an inequality in x and solve it to find the maximum number of sandwiches he can make.

5 A TV repair man charges a call-out fee of £40 and £24 per hour for each hour that he works.

a) Write down an expression for his total charge when he works x hours.

b) For one job he receives £136.
Write down an equation in x and solve it to find how many hours the job took.

6 The diagram below shows a plan of Alicia's garden.

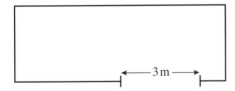

Alicia wants to put a fence round the garden leaving a gateway 3 metres wide.
Fence panels are 2 metres wide.
The garden has a total perimeter of 56 metres.
Let x be the number of fence panels.
Write down an inequality in x and solve it to find the smallest number of fence panels that Alicia must buy.

STAG
7

14 Compound measures

STAGE
7

EXERCISE 14.1H

1 A car travels 90 miles in 2 hours.
What is its average speed?

2 A chocolate has a mass of 30 g.
Its volume is 2·5 cm³.
What is its density?

3 Green Borough has a population of 86 000 and an
area of 160 km².
Calculate its population density.
Give your answer correct to 1 decimal place.

4 A town has a population of 74 000 and an area of
64 km².
Calculate the population density of the town.
Give your answer correct to 1 decimal place.

5 A train is travelling at 22 metres per second.
How far does it travel in 1 minute?

6 A runner's average speed is 3·2 metres per second.
How long does it take her to run 1 km?

7 An iron bar has a mass of 1750 g and a density of
7 g/cm³.
Calculate its volume.

8 Gold has a density of 19·3 g/cm³.
Calculate the mass of a gold bar with a volume of
1000 cm³.
Give your answer in kilograms.

9 a) Calculate the density of a 3 cm³ block of copper
with a mass of 26·7 g.

b) What would be the mass of a 17 cm³ block of copper?

10 a) Find the speed of a car which travels 75 km in
1 hour 15 minutes.

b) A car travels 15 km in 14 minutes.
Find its speed in kilometres per hour.
Give your answer correct to 1 decimal place.

Reciprocals, factors and multiples

EXERCISE 15.1H

Do not use your calculator for questions **1** to **3**.

1 Write down the reciprocal of each of these numbers.

   a) 3   **b)** 6   **c)** 49   **d)** 100   **e)** 640

2 Write down the number of which each of these is the reciprocal.

   a) $\frac{1}{16}$ **b)** $\frac{1}{9}$ **c)** $\frac{1}{52}$ **d)** $\frac{1}{67}$ **e)** $\frac{1}{1000}$

3 Calculate the reciprocal of each of these numbers, giving your answer as a fraction or a mixed number.

   a) $\frac{4}{5}$ **b)** $\frac{3}{8}$ **c)** $1\frac{3}{5}$ **d)** $3\frac{1}{3}$ **e)** $\frac{2}{25}$

You may use your calculator for question **4**.

4 Calculate the reciprocal of each of these numbers, giving your answer as a decimal.

   a) 2·5   **b)** 0·2   **c)** 125   **d)** 0·16   **e)** 3·2

EXERCISE 15.2H

1 a) Express each of these numbers as a product of its prime factors.

    (i) 14   **(ii)** 16   **(iii)** 28   **(iv)** 35   **(v)** 42

  b) Use your results from part **a)** to find each of these.
    (i)   The HCF of 14 and 35
    (ii) The LCM of 16 and 42
    (iii) The HCF of 16 and 42
    (iv) The LCM of 28 and 35

2 a) Decompose each of these numbers into its prime factors.

    (i) 49   **(ii)** 108   **(iii)** 156   **(iv)** 225   **(v)** 424

  b) Use your results from part **a)** to find each of these.
    (i)   The HCF of 49 and 108
    (ii) The LCM of 108 and 156
    (iii) The HCF of 156 and 225
    (iv) The LCM of 225 and 424

3 Find the prime factors of these numbers and use this to write
down the HCF and LCM of each pair.

  a) 84 and 154

  b) 75 and 135

4 Find the HCF and the LCM of each pair of numbers.

  a) 17 and 40

  b) 52 and 221

  c) 77 and 98

Circles and tangents

16

Give your answers to these questions as simply as possible.
Leave π in your answers where appropriate.

1 Simplify each of these.

a) $2 \times 6 \times \pi$

b) $\pi \times 7^2$

c) $\pi \times 12^2$

d) $2 \times 3 \cdot 8 \times \pi$

e) $\pi \times 11^2$

2 Simplify each of these.

a) $14\pi + 5\pi$

b) $\pi \times 3^2 + \pi \times 6^2$

c) $\pi \times 8^2 - \pi \times 4^2$

d) $3 \times 42\pi$

e) $\dfrac{36\pi}{4\pi}$

3 Find the circumference of a circle with radius 15 cm.

4 The areas of two circles are in the ratio $36\pi : 16\pi$.
Simplify this ratio.

5 A circular piece of card has radius 12 cm.
A square piece with sides of 5 cm is removed.
Find the area of card that is left.

STAGE

7

EXERCISE 16.2H

Use this diagram for questions **1** to **4**.

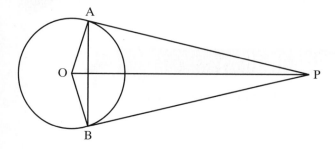

1 Given that angle AOP = 58°, find

   a) angle APO.   **b)** angle PBA.

2 Calculate angle AOB when angle APB = 76°.

3 Given that angle PAB = 69°, find

   a) angle APO.   **b)** angle AOB.

4 Calculate the radius of the circle, OA, when AP = 10 cm and OP = 12 cm.

Changing the subject of a formula

17

1 Rearrange each formula to make the letter in brackets the subject.

a) $a + b + c = 180$ $\qquad$ (*b*)

b) $x = 5y + z$ $\qquad$ (*y*)

c) $A = \dfrac{bh}{2}$ $\qquad$ (*h*)

d) $a = 180(n - 2)$ $\qquad$ (*n*)

e) $c = p - 3t$ $\qquad$ (*t*)

f) $A = p(q + r)$ $\qquad$ (*q*)

g) $p = 2g - 2f$ $\qquad$ (*g*)

h) $F = \dfrac{m + 4n}{t}$ $\qquad$ (*n*)

2 To change from degrees Celsius (°C) to degrees Fahrenheit (°F), you can use the formula $F = \frac{9}{5}(C + 40) - 40$.

a) The temperature is 60°C. What is this in °F?

b) Rearrange the formula to find C in terms of F.

c) The temperature is 98°F. What is this in °C?

3 The surface area of a sphere is given by the formula $A = 4\pi r^2$.

a) Find the surface area of a sphere with a radius of 4 cm.

b) Rearrange the formula to make r the subject.

c) Find the radius of a sphere with a surface area of 147 cm².

STAG
7

18 Equations and inequalities 2

EXERCISE 18.1H

pt

Solve these equations.

1 $2(x - 3) = x$

2 $3(2x + 1) = 27$

3 $3(x - 4) = 36$

4 $3(4 + x) = 21$

5 $6(x - 6) = 6$

6 $4(x + 3) = 16$

7 $2(x - 8) = 14$

8 $2(x + 4) = 10$

9 $2(x - 4) = 20$

10 $5(x + 1) = 30$

11 $7x - 4 = 3x + 8$

12 $5x + 4 = 2x + 13$

13 $6x - 2 = x + 8$

14 $5x + 1 = 3x + 21$

15 $9x - 10 = 3x + 8$

16 $5x - 12 = 2x - 6$

17 $4x - 23 = x + 7$

18 $8x + 8 = 3x - 2$

19 $2 \cdot 3x = 9 \cdot 43$

20 $5 \cdot 4(x - 3) = 3 \cdot 78$

EXERCISE 18.2H

Solve these inequalities.

1 $x - 2 > 1$

2 $x + 1 < 3$

3 $3x - 2 \geqslant 7$

4 $2x + 1 \leqslant 6$

5 $3x - 6 \geqslant 0$

6 $7 \leqslant 2x - 1$

7 $5x < x + 12$

8 $4x \geqslant x + 9$

9 $4 + x < 0$

10 $3x + 1 \leqslant 2x + 6$

11 $2(x - 3) > x$

12 $5(x + 1) > 3x + 10$

13 $7x + 5 \leqslant 2x + 30$

14 $5x + 2 < 7x - 4$

15 $3(3x + 2) \geqslant 2(x + 10)$

EXERCISE 18.3H

1 6 subtracted from 3 times a number gives an answer of 18.
Use x to represent the number.
Write down and solve an equation to find x.

2 Lauren thinks of a number.
She multiplies it by 3 and then subtracts 5. The answer is 10.
Use x to represent Lauren's number.
Write down and solve an equation to find Lauren's number.

3 Jack thinks of a number.
He multiplies it by 10, then he adds 5. The answer is 95.
Use x to represent Jack's number.
Write down and solve an equation to find Jack's number.

4 Emma thinks of a number.
She doubles it. The answer is $^{-}52$.
Use x to represent Emma's number.
Write down and solve an equation to find Emma's number.

5 A number and twice the number add up to 9.
Let the number be x.
Write down and solve an equation to find x.

6 Three angles of a triangle are $x°$, $(2x - 40)°$ and $70°$.
Write down an equation in x and solve it to find the angles of the triangle.

7 A number plus 7 is the same as twice the number minus 8.
Let the number be x.
Write down and solve an equation to find x.

8 A rectangle has a length of x and a width of $2x - 9$.
The perimeter of the rectangle is 12 cm.
Write down an equation in x and solve it to find the dimensions of the rectangle.

STAGE

7

19 Loci

EXERCISE 19.1H

1 Draw a line 8 cm long.
Draw the locus of points which are 2 cm from the line.

2 Draw an angle of 110°.
Construct the bisector of the angle.

3 Construct a triangle with sides of length 9 cm, 8 cm and 6 cm.
Construct the bisectors of each of the three angles.
What do you notice?

4 Draw a rectangle ABCD with sides AB = 8 cm and BC = 5 cm.
Show by shading the locus of points inside the rectangle which are nearer BA than BC.

5 Construct a triangle ABC with AB = 10 cm, BC = 8 cm and AC = 5 cm.
Show by shading the locus of points which are inside the triangle and nearer to A than B.

EXERCISE 19.2H

1 Draw a triangle ABC with AB = 8 cm, AC = 6 cm
and angle $A = 70°$.
Find, by construction, the point D which is equidistant from B and
C and is also 5 cm from C.

2 Draw a line AB.
Mark the point O, 5 cm below the line AB.
Show, by shading, the locus of points which are less than 2 cm
from the line AB and also less than 4 cm from the point O.

3 The diagram shows a swimming pool 50 m long by 20 m wide.

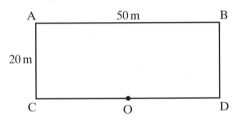

The shallow end extends to a distance 20 m from AC.
Amanda's mother is at O, halfway along CD.

a) Using a scale of 1 cm to 5 m, make a scale drawing of the pool.

b) Amanda's mother says Amanda can swim anywhere in the
shallow end or within 15 m of her.
Show by shading all the places that Amanda can swim.

STAGE

7

4 Construct a triangle ABC with AB = 11 cm, AC = 7 cm and
BC = 9 cm.
Show, by construction, the locus of points inside the triangle
which are equidistant from A and B and also nearer AB than AC.

5 Draw a rectangle ABCD with AB = 10 cm and AD = 6 cm.
Show, by construction, the locus of points inside the rectangle for
which all these statements are true.

a) The points are nearer to D than A.

b) The points are nearer to DC than DA.

c) The points are less than 7 cm from A.

20 Decimals

EXERCISE 20.1H

1 Work out these.

a) $3\cdot6 \times 4$ b) $5\cdot8 \times 6$ c) $0\cdot5 \times 0\cdot7$

d) $2\cdot3 \times 6\cdot4$ e) $4\cdot3 \times 1\cdot8$ f) $14\cdot2 \times 5\cdot8$

g) $7\cdot9 \times 6\cdot2$ h) $21\cdot3 \times 4\cdot3$ i) $5\cdot23 \times 0\cdot4$

j) $3\cdot72 \times 1\cdot5$ k) $6\cdot72 \times 4\cdot92$ l) $1\cdot78 \times 3\cdot25$

2 Work out these.

a) $23\cdot6 \div 4$ b) $23\cdot4 \div 3$ c) $16\cdot2 \div 0\cdot3$

d) $32\cdot8 \div 0\cdot4$ e) $51\cdot1 \div 0\cdot7$ f) $82\cdot8 \div 1\cdot8$

g) $3\cdot12 \div 0\cdot4$ h) $22\cdot08 \div 3\cdot2$ i) $5\cdot16 \div 1\cdot2$

j) $13\cdot23 \div 6\cdot3$ k) $36\cdot24 \div 0\cdot8$ l) $29\cdot25 \div 3\cdot25$

EXERCISE 20.2H

Convert each of the fractions in questions **1** to **14** to a decimal. When the answer is a recurring decimal, use the dot notation.

1 $\frac{37}{100}$ **2** $\frac{3}{5}$ **3** $\frac{2}{3}$ **4** $\frac{3}{20}$ **5** $\frac{1}{8}$ **6** $\frac{2}{9}$ **7** $\frac{7}{16}$

8 $\frac{13}{50}$ **9** $\frac{41}{66}$ **10** $\frac{83}{250}$ **11** $\frac{43}{125}$ **12** $\frac{10}{11}$ **13** $\frac{14}{15}$ **14** $\frac{18}{111}$

15 Put these fractions in order, smallest first.

$\frac{1}{2}, \frac{2}{5}, \frac{3}{7}, \frac{4}{11}, \frac{9}{16}, \frac{9}{19}$

EXERCISE 20.3H

Convert each of these to a fraction in its lowest terms.

1 $0\cdot23$ **2** $0\cdot6$ **3** $0\cdot95$ **4** $0\cdot008$ **5** $0\cdot04$

6 $0\cdot175$ **7** $0\cdot\dot{3}$ **8** $0\cdot\dot{5}$ **9** $0\cdot0\dot{1}$ **10** $0\cdot0\dot{6}$

Accuracy

21

1 Identify whether each data item is discrete or continuous.

a) The distance from Nottingham to Cambridge is 160 km.

b) A car engine has a capacity of 2 litres.

c) A car engine has 16 valves.

d) There are 15 light bulbs in a room.

e) The power of a light bulb is 100 watts.

2 Read this description.
Write the underlined items under the correct heading in a copy of this table.

Discrete	Continuous

STAGE

7

> James is 1·93 m tall and weighs 74 kg. Jim gained
> 6 GCSEs last summer and got a job in a bank.
> He travels 3·7 km to work each morning; the
> journey usually takes him 20 minutes. Though he
> is only paid £180 a week, he does manage to save
> some of it. He loves the hot weather and is saving
> to go on holiday. James and his 4 friends can't
> wait to get away. His Dad is taking them to the
> airport and is only going to charge them for the
> 32 litres of petrol he will need. At 907 km/h the
> aircraft will quickly get its 432 passengers to their
> destination.

‖‖‖ EXERCISE 21.2H

1 Give the lower and upper bounds of each of these measurements.

a) Given to the nearest centimetre
    (i) 15 cm   **(ii)** 90 cm   **(iii)** 300 cm   **(iv)** 2·17 m

b) Given to the nearest millimetre
    (i) 0·2 cm   **(ii)** 5·9 cm   **(iii)** 6·0 cm   **(iv)** 3·162 m

c) Given to the nearest 10 cm
    (i) 90 cm   **(ii)** 200 cm   **(iii)** 5·3 m   **(iv)** 200 mm

d) Given to the nearest hundredth of a second
    (i) 9·83 seconds   **(ii)** 87·08 seconds   **(iii)** 23·80 seconds

2 Copy and complete each of these statements.

a) A length given as 4·3 cm to 1 decimal place is between … cm and … cm.

b) A capacity given as 463 ml to the nearest millilitre is between … ml and … ml.

c) A time given as 10·5 seconds to the nearest tenth of a second is between … seconds and … seconds.

d) A mass given as 78 kg to the nearest kilogram is between … kg and … kg.

e) An area given as 5·5 m² to 1 decimal place is between … m² and … m².

f) A height given as 142 cm to the nearest centimetre is between … cm and … cm.

g) A height given as 75·0 cm to 1 decimal place is between … cm and … cm.

h) A length given as 7·83 mm to 2 decimal places is between … mm and … mm.

Indices

pt

1 Write these in a simpler form, using indices.

  a) $2 \times 2 \times 2 \times 2$

  b) $2 \times 2 \times 3 \times 3 \times 5 \times 5 \times 5$

  c) $a \times a \times a \times a \times a$

2 Write these in a simpler form, using indices.

  a) $2^6 \times 2^5$ **b)** $3^6 \times 3^2$

  c) $4^2 \times 4^3$ **d)** $5^6 \times 5$

3 Write these in a simpler form, using indices.

  a) $5^5 \div 5^2$ **b)** $7^8 \div 7^2$

  c) $2^6 \div 2^4$ **d)** $3^7 \div 3^3$

4 Work out these, giving your answers in index form.

  a) $\dfrac{2^5 \times 2^4}{2^3}$ **b)** $\dfrac{3^7}{3^5 \times 3^2}$

  c) $\dfrac{5^5 \times 5^4}{5^2 \times 5^3}$ **d)** $\dfrac{7^5 \times 7^2}{7^2 \times 7^4}$

5 Simplify these.

  a) $a^4 \times 2a^2$ **b)** $a^5 \div a^3$

  c) $3a^3 \times 4a^2$ **d)** $12a^3 \div 4a^2$

STAG

7

EXERCISE 22.2H

Do not use your calculator for questions **1** to **5**.

1 Write down the square of each number.

    a) 9   **b)** 70   **c)** $\sqrt{13}$

2 Write down the square root of each number.

    a) 225   **b)** 1600   **c)** 83^2

3 Write down the cube of each number.

    a) 1   **b)** 2   **c)** $\sqrt[3]{54}$

4 Write down the cube root of each number.

    a) 27   **b)** 1 000 000   **c)** 62^3

5 A cube has sides of length 4 cm. What is its volume?

You may use your calculator for questions **6** to **10**.

6 Find the square of each of these numbers.

    a) 20   **b)** 42   **c)** 5·1

    d) 60   **e)** 0·9

7 Find the square root of each of these numbers.
  Where necessary, give your answer correct to 2 decimal places.

    a) 900   **b)** 75   **c)** 284

    d) 31 684   **e)** 40 401

8 Find the cube of each of these numbers.

    a) 7   **b)** 3·5   **c)** 9·4

    d) 20   **e)** 100

9 Find the cube root of each of these numbers.
  Where necessary, give your answer correct to 2 decimal places.

    a) 729   **b)** 144   **c)** 9·261

    d) 4848   **e)** 100 000

10 A square has an area of 80 cm². What is the length of its sides?
  Give your answer correct to 2 decimal places.

Trial and improvement

23

1 Show that a solution of $x^3 - 2x - 1 = 0$ lies between 1 and 2.
Use trial and improvement to find the solution correct to 1 decimal place.

2 Show that a solution of $x^3 + 5x - 3 = 0$ lies between 0 and 1.
Use trial and improvement to find the solution correct to 1 decimal place.

3 Show that a solution of $x^3 - 5x + 2 = 0$ lies between $^-3$ and $^-2$.
Use trial and improvement to find the solution correct to 1 decimal place.

4 Show that the equation $x^3 - 5x + 2 = 0$ has another solution between 0 and 1.
Use trial and improvement to find this solution correct to 1 decimal place.

STAG

7

24 Sequences

You may find the example useful for all of these exercises.

▌▐║ EXERCISE 24.1H

Which of these sequences are linear and which are not?
For each sequence, write down the next two terms.

1 4, 8, 12, 16, …   4 3, 6, 11, 18, …

2 45, 40, 36, 33, …   5 1, 9, 17, 25, …

3 28, 25, 22, 19, …

▌▐║ EXERCISE 24.2H

Each of these is the formula for the nth term of a sequence.
Find the first four terms of each sequence.

1 $n + 6$ 6 $3n - 2$

2 $6n$ 7 $4n + 4$

3 $n - 2$ 8 ^-n

4 $3n + 2$ 9 $5n + 2$

5 $2n - 7$ 10 $1 - 2n$

▌▐║ EXERCISE 24.3H

Find the formula for the nth term for each of these sequences.

1 2, 4, 6, 8, …   6 10, 13, 16, 19, …

2 4, 7, 10, 13, …   7 $^-3, ^-1, 1, 3, …$

3 0, 3, 6, 9, …   8 25, 20, 15, 10, …

4 21, 22, 23, 24, …   9 4, 2, 0, $^-2$, …

5 1, 5, 9, 13, …   10 3, 2, 1, 0, …

Multiplying out two brackets

EXERCISE 25.1H

Multiply out the brackets.

1 $(x + 1)(x + 2)$ **6** $(x + 1)(x - 5)$

2 $(x + 3)(x + 4)$ **7** $(x + 3)(x - 3)$

3 $(x + 2)(x - 1)$ **8** $(x + 2)^2$

4 $(x + 5)(x - 3)$ **9** $(x - 7)^2$

5 $(x - 1)(x - 2)$ **10** $(x - 12)(x - 9)$

STAG

7

Prisms and units

1 Find the volume of each of these prisms.

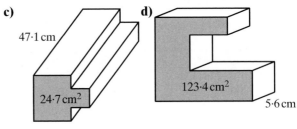

a)

b)

49·7 cm²   16·4 cm

97·3 cm²   9·4 cm

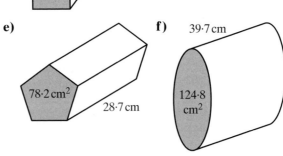

c)

47·1 cm

24·7 cm²

d)

123·4 cm²   5·6 cm

e)

78·2 cm²   28·7 cm

f)   39·7 cm

124·8 cm²

2 Calculate the volume of this cylinder.

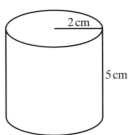

2 cm

5 cm